My first

I can draw...

Wild Animals

Follow the simple steps
to learn how to draw lots
of charming characters.

•

Tear out the practice pages
to perfect your pictures before
drawing them in the scenes.

Hissing **snakes**

Try drawing your own . . .

1

Draw a long,
wiggly body.

2

Add a head and
a forked tongue.

3

Draw stripes at the
end of the tail.

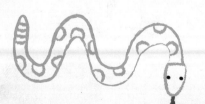

4

Give the
slithery snake
patterned scales.

Sleepy **sloths**

1

Draw an oval for the head and part of a semicircle for the body.

2

Add two long legs.

3

Draw two eye patches and add little claws to the legs.

4

Give the sleepy sloth a sweet face.

Try drawing your own . . .

Hungry hippos

1
Draw a circle for the body and add two legs.

2
Draw an oval for the nose and add two nostrils. Add toenails to the feet.

3
Draw a semicircle for the head.

4
Give the happy hippo two eyes and two oval ears.

Try drawing your own...

Mischievous monkeys

1 Draw a circle for the tummy.

2 Add an oval for the mouth and a semicircle for the head.

Try drawing your own . . .

3 Give the monkey two semicircles for ears and a cheerful face.

4 Draw four lines for the arms and legs.

5 Add a curly line for the tail.

Grizzly **bears**

1 Draw the head and the body.

2 Add two semicircles for the ears and draw a small tail.

Try drawing your own . . .

3 Draw four lines for the legs.

4 Add a circle for the snout.

5 Give the grizzly bear a happy face.

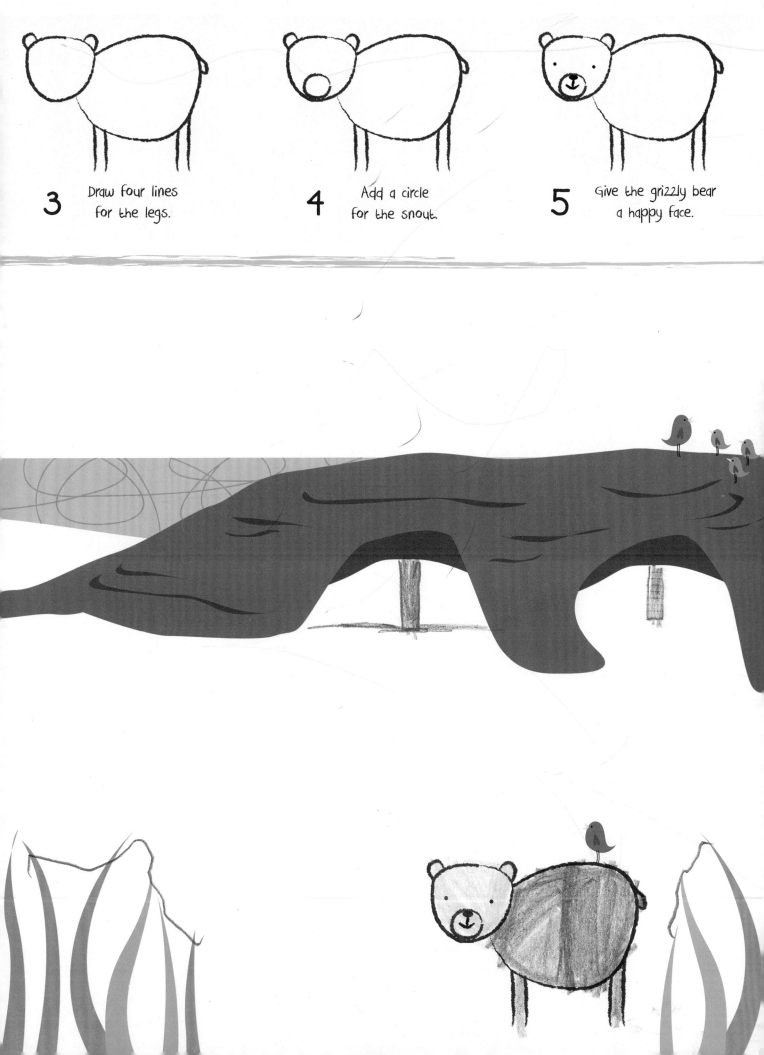

Perching **parrots**

1

Draw a circle for
the head and
add the body.

2

Add a big,
curved beak and
a feathery tail.

3

Draw a fluffy wing
and two little feet.

4

Give the parrot
a face and
bright feathers.

Fuzzy **pandas**

1

Draw a circle for the head and add two long arms.

2

Add the tummy and a stripe. Draw two semicircles for the ears.

3

Add two ovals for the feet.

4

Give the playful panda a fuzzy face with two circles for the eye patches.

Try drawing your own . . .

Prowling leopards

1 Draw a curved rectangle for the body.

2 Add four lines for the legs.

Try drawing your own . . .

3 Draw the head.

4 Add two semicircles for the ears and a curved line for the tail.

5 Give the Leopard lots of spots and a face.

Enormous **elephants**

1

Draw a rectangle for the body.

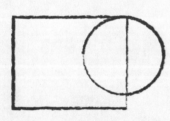

2

Add a circle across the rectangle to make the head and ear.

3

Add two rectangles for the legs and add a long trunk.

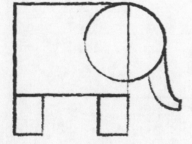

4

Give the elephant a long tail, an eye, and some toenails.

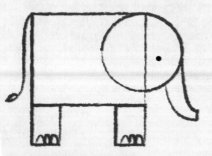

Try drawing your own . . .

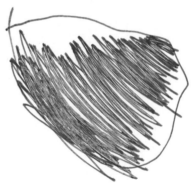

Chilly polar bears

1 Draw the head and the body.

2 Add two semicircles for the feet.

Try drawing your own . . .

3 Draw the legs.

4 Add two semicircles for the ears.

5 Give the polar bear two cute eyes and a big, black nose.

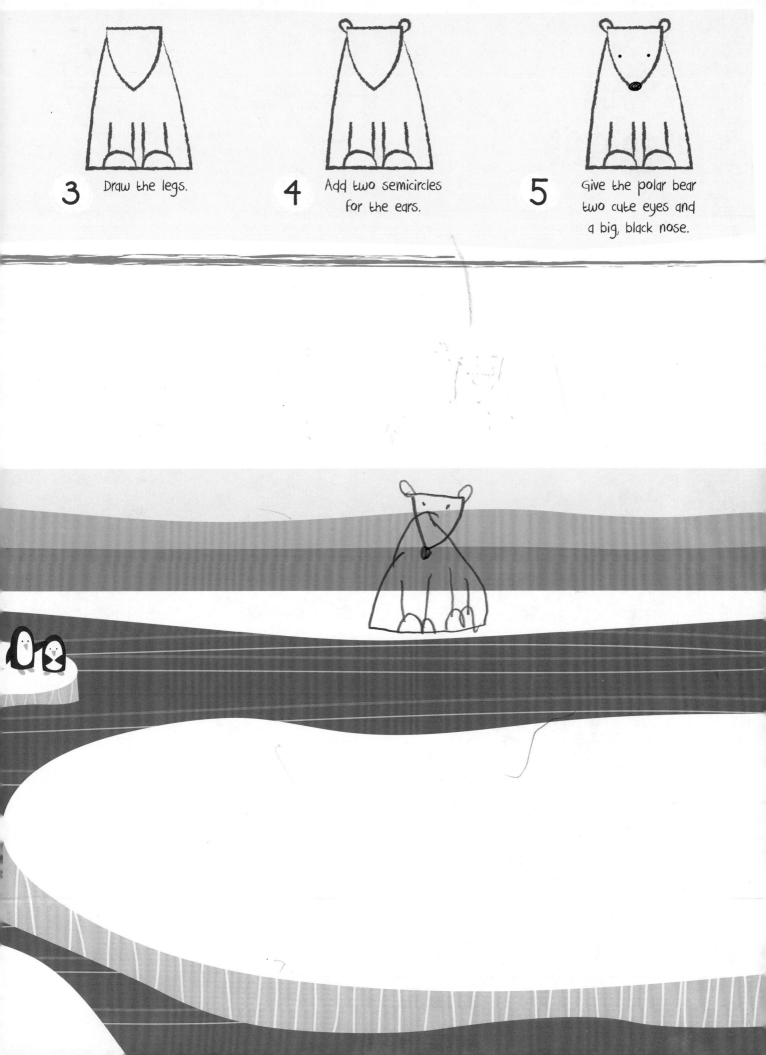

Zany zebras

1 Draw a semicircle for the body.

2 Add a long neck and a head.

Try drawing your own . . .

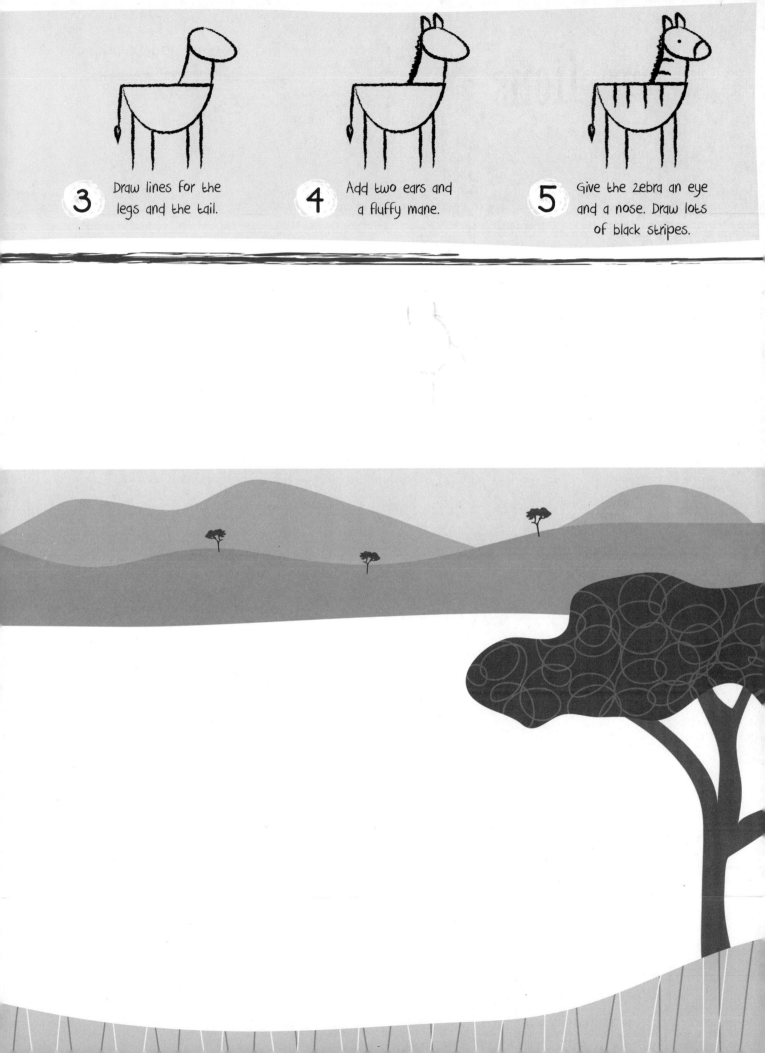

3 Draw lines for the legs and the tail.

4 Add two ears and a fluffy mane.

5 Give the zebra an eye and a nose. Draw lots of black stripes.

Leaping lions

1

Draw a circle for the head and add a curly mane.

2

Add the body and two semicircles for the ears.

3

Draw four legs and a tail.

4

Give the lion a fierce face and a fluffy tail.

Try drawing your own . . .

Fierce **tigers**

1

Draw a rectangle
for the body and
a long semicircle
for the head.

2

Add two semicircles
for the ears and
draw four lines
for the legs.

3

Draw a curved line
for the tail.

4

Give the tiger
a cute face
and lots of
terrific stripes.

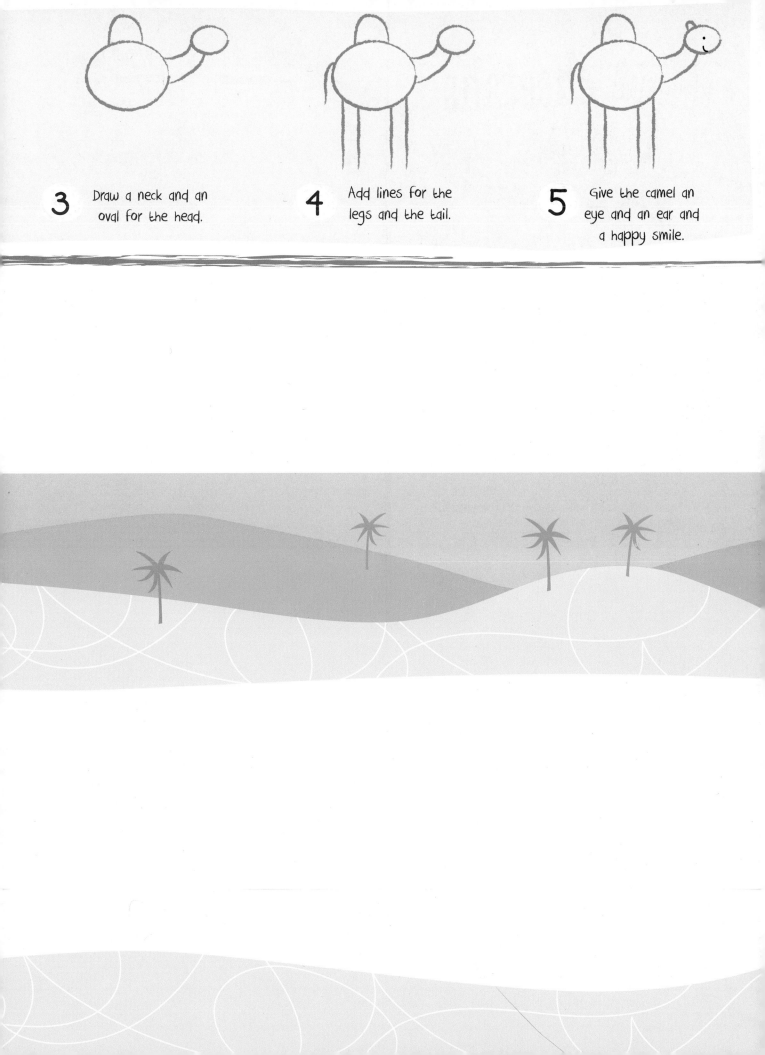

3 Draw a neck and an oval for the head.

4 Add lines for the legs and the tail.

5 Give the camel an eye and an ear and a happy smile.

Cheerful **cheetahs**

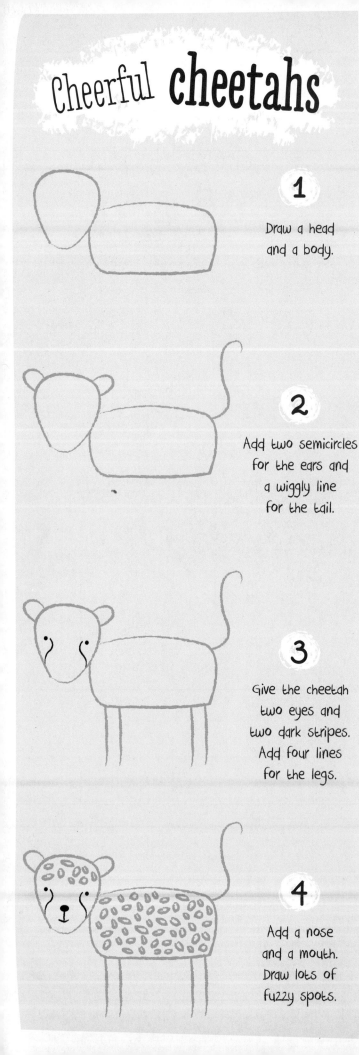

1

Draw a head and a body.

2

Add two semicircles for the ears and a wiggly line for the tail.

3

Give the cheetah two eyes and two dark stripes. Add four lines for the legs.

4

Add a nose and a mouth. Draw lots of fuzzy spots.

Try drawing your own...

Muddy rhinos

1 Draw a rectangle for the body and add the head.

2 Add two ears and a tail.

Try drawing your own . . .

3 Draw two rectangles for the legs.

4 Add a horn on the rhino's nose.

5 Give the rhino two eyes, two nostrils, and a big smile!

Giant giraffes

Try drawing your own . . .

1

Draw a head and
a very long neck.

2

Draw a rectangle
for the body
and add two ears.

3

Add lines for the
legs and the tail.
Draw two horns.

4

Give the giant
giraffe two eyes
and two nostrils.
Add lots of spots.

Kicking kangaroos

1

Draw an oval
for the head
and add a neck.

2

Add a large oval
for the body, two
ears, an arm, and
two legs.

3

Give the kangaroo
a comfy pouch,
a long tail,
and a cute face.

Goofy gorillas

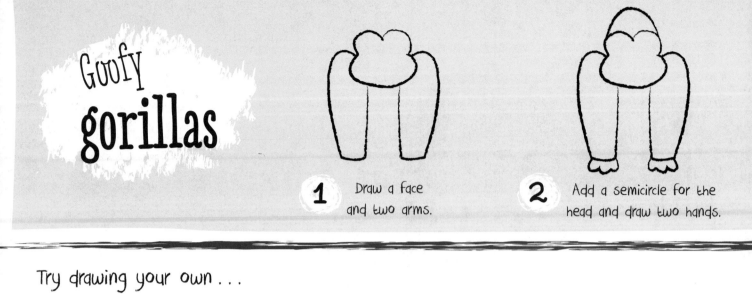

1 Draw a face and two arms.

2 Add a semicircle for the head and draw two hands.

Try drawing your own...

3 Finish the body and draw two back legs.

4 Draw two ears.

5 Give the gorilla a happy face.

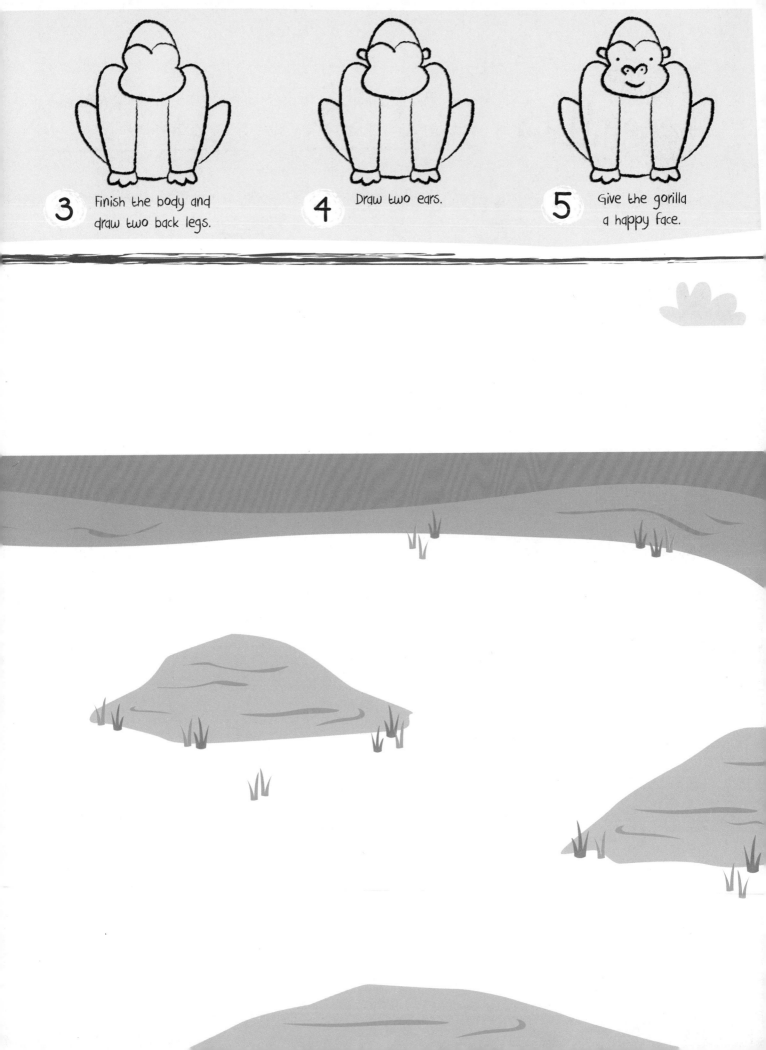

Scaly crocodiles

1 Draw a semicircle for the body.

2 Add a tail and lots of spikes.

Try drawing your own . . .

3 Draw the head and add a semicircle for the eye.

4 Give the crocodile lots of sharp teeth.